A Time for Friends

A Time for Friends

Eldonna L. Evertts / Language Arts
Lyman C. Hunt / Reading
Bernard J. Weiss / Linguistics and Curriculum

Edited by Jane Berkowitz and Craig Bettinger
Educational Consultants: Patsy Montague and Janet Sprout

THE HOLT BASIC READING SYSTEM · LEVEL 8 ·

HOLT, RINEHART AND WINSTON, INC.
New York / Toronto / London / Sydney

Illustrated by

Marie Michal, pages 14–27
Ethel Gold, pages 28–46, 188–199
Diane de Groat, pages 47, 153–155, 186–187, 190
Lester Abrams, pages 48–62
Phil Smith, pages 64–83
Ellen Olean, page 84
Tom Leigh, pages 88–105
Marvin Mattelson, page 106
Tim and Greg Hildebrandt, page 107
Lionel Kalish, pages 108–121, 171–185
Viewpoint Graphics, Inc., pages 122, 201
Blair Drawson, pages 123–133
Tad Krumeich, pages 134–144
Bernice Myers, pages 158–170
George Senty, photos: pages 188–200
Tom Upshur, pages 202–215
Norman Green, pages 216–229
Cover, pages 6–13, 86–87, and 156–157 designed by Katherine
    Wanous; constructed by S. N. Studio.

Acknowledgments

Grateful acknowledgment is made to the following authors and publishers:

Child Life and Elizabeth Upham McWebb for "At Mrs. Appleby's." Copyright
1944 by Elizabeth Upham McWebb. Used by permission.

Contents

All Kinds of Friends

All Kinds of Families

All Kinds of Places to Go

All Kinds of Friends

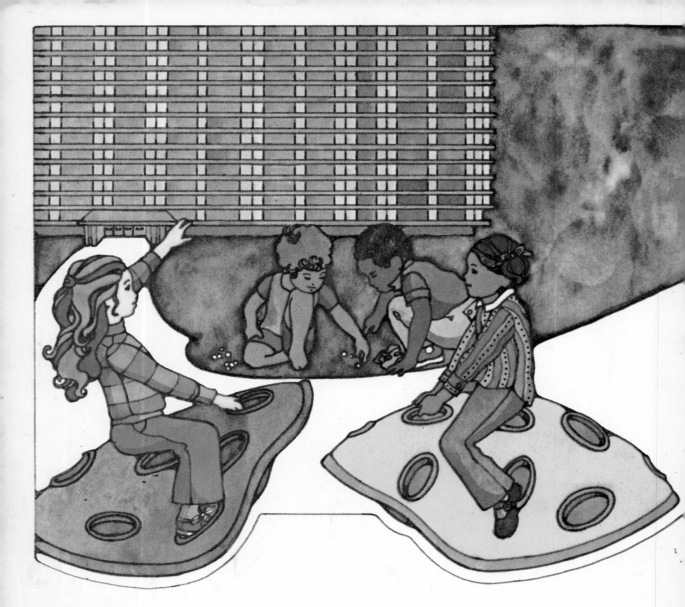

Kim
and
Rosa

Kim lived in a big apartment house.
She lived in apartment 17B
with her mother and daddy
and sister and brother.
Kim had lots of friends
in the apartment house.

One of Kim's friends was Rosa.
She lived in apartment 6B.
When Kim wanted to go to Rosa's,
her big sister had to take her.
When it was time to go home,
Kim's sister had to come and get her.

Kim didn't like to have
her sister take her places.
She wanted to go alone.

But her mother said she was too little.

One day Kim's sister was not at home
when Kim wanted to go to see Rosa.

"Will you take me to Rosa's, Mother?"
asked Kim.

Mother said, "I don't have time
to take you, Kim.

But you are a big girl now.

You can go alone."

That was all Kim's mother had to say.
Kim ran out of her apartment.

She was going to Rosa's alone!

The girls played at Rosa's all morning.
Then Rosa's brother came home
with some friends.

"Boys make too much noise," said Kim.
"Do you want to go up to my apartment?
It's quiet there."

"Yes," said Rosa.
"Let me tell Mother where I'm going."

The Elevator

Kim and Rosa got into the elevator.
They looked at all the buttons.
They tried to reach the one that said 17.
But they couldn't reach it.

"What are we going to do?"
asked Rosa.

"Maybe if I jump, I can reach 17,"
said Kim.

Kim jumped up.
She did reach a button, but not 17.

The elevator went up to

7, 8, 9, 10

21

11, 12, 13. . . .

Then it stopped, and the door opened.

"This is not my floor," said Kim.

"Let me jump up," said Rosa.
"Maybe I can reach 17."

Rosa tried, but she didn't reach 17.
This time the elevator went down to **12,**

11,

10.

Then it stopped.
And the door opened.

"This is not my floor," said Kim.

The girls tried again and again.
The elevator went up and down.
But it did not go to Kim's floor.
Kim tried to reach the button again.
This time the elevator went down to **6.**

"This is **my** floor," said Rosa.

Rosa got out of the elevator.
"I'll be back," she said to Kim.

"What are you going to do?"
asked Kim.
"Are you going to get someone?"

"No," said Rosa.
"We can go up to 17 alone.
You will see."

Rosa ran into her apartment.
She came back with a big book.

Rosa and Kim got into the elevator.
Rosa put the book on the floor
by the buttons.
Kim got up on the book.
This time she did reach 17.
The elevator went up to

7, 8, 9, 10, 11, 12,

13, 14, 15, 16, 17...

Then it stopped.
And the door opened.

"This is my floor," said Kim.

Rosa picked up her book.
The two girls got out of the elevator
and went to Kim's apartment to play.

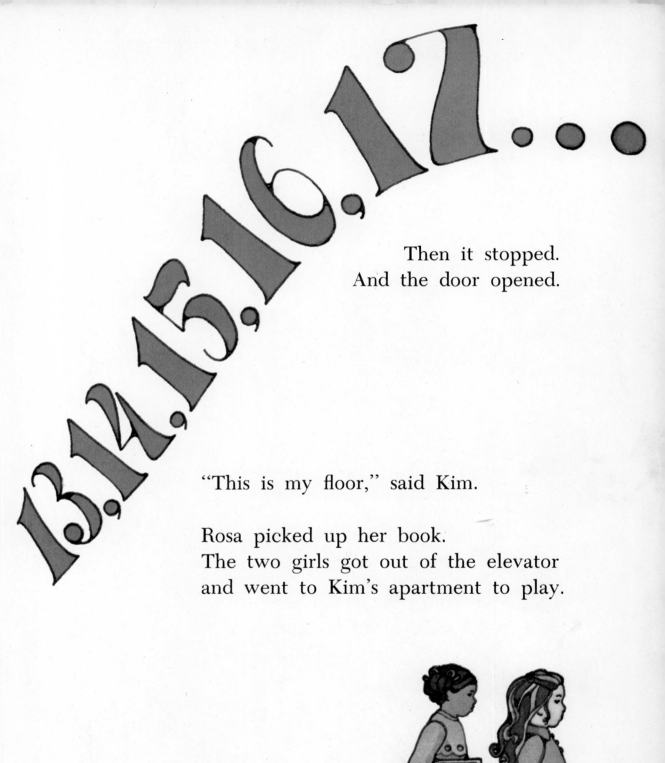

Annie Moorecroft

Two Friends

Edward and Peter were old friends.
When they were little,
they played all day.
One day they would play
at Edward's house.
The next day they would play
at Peter's house.
Some nights Edward would sleep
at Peter's house.
And some nights Peter would sleep
at Edward's house.

When they got big,
the boys went to school.
At school they played and worked
like old friends.
Peter would read to Edward.
Edward would read to Peter.

Sometimes after school, Peter would go
to Edward's house for cookies.
Sometimes they would go to Peter's house.
Peter's mother would have apples
for the boys.
People said that Peter and Edward were
like brothers.

One morning Edward went
to Peter's house.
Peter's mother came to the door.

"Peter is sick," she said.
"He won't be going to school."

"That's too bad," said Edward.

Edward went to school alone.
He played with some friends.
He looked at pictures with them.
But it was a bad day for Edward.
He was lonely.
He wanted to be with Peter.

After school Edward went home.
He had no one to play with
but his dog.

"Do you get lonely when I'm at school?"
he asked his dog.

"He gets lonely in the afternoon,"
said Edward's mother.
"That's when he looks for you.
He wants you to come home."

"I'll play with you," said Edward.
"You won't have to be lonely."

Edward played with his dog all afternoon.
But it was a lonely day.
He wanted to be with Peter, too.

The next morning Edward went
to Peter's house.
Peter came to the door.

"I'm all right this morning,"
he said.
"I'm going to school."

"That's good," said Edward.
"I was lonely when you were sick."

"We can play at my house
after school," said Peter.

"No," said Edward.
"We have to go to my house.
Then we can play with my dog.
He gets lonely, too."

The New Boy

One day when Edward went to Peter's,
he did not go alone.

"This is my new friend, Jimmy,"
he said to Peter.
"He lives in the new house next door.
And he has a cat."

The boys went to school.
Jimmy told Edward about his cat.
And Edward told Jimmy about his dog.

Edward said, "Peter has a frog."

Peter told Jimmy about his frog.

"Don't let my cat see your frog,"
said Jimmy.
"Cats don't like frogs."

Peter didn't like it
when Jimmy said that.

At school Edward and Jimmy looked
at pictures.
Edward asked Peter to look
at the pictures, too.

"No," said Peter.
"I don't like Jimmy.
I don't want to play with him.
If you like Jimmy,
then you can't be my friend."

"If I can't be your friend,
then you can't be my friend,"
said Edward.

37

That morning Peter didn't read
to Edward.
And Edward didn't read to Peter.
After school Peter didn't go
to Edward's house.
He went home alone.

"Where is Edward?" Peter's mother asked.

"Edward has a new friend,"
said Peter.
"He isn't going to come here to play.
He's at Jimmy's house."

"Who is Jimmy?" asked Peter's mother.

"He's a new boy," said Peter.
"And he's Edward's new friend."

"Can't Jimmy be your friend, too?
Can't all three of you play?"
asked Peter's mother.

"No," said Peter.
"I don't like Jimmy.
He isn't my friend.
And Edward isn't my friend.
And I don't want to play with them!"

Three Friends

The next day Peter walked
to school alone.
Edward walked with Jimmy.

At school Peter read books
and looked at pictures.
But it was no fun without Edward.

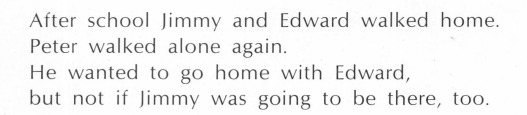

After school Jimmy and Edward walked home.
Peter walked alone again.
He wanted to go home with Edward,
but not if Jimmy was going to be there, too.

Jimmy and Edward stopped
at Jimmy's house.
Peter walked on by.
But Edward saw him.

"Peter, where are you going?"
asked Edward.

"Home," said Peter.

"Would you like to see Jimmy's cat?"
asked Edward.
"He's in the house."

"Yes," said Jimmy to Peter.
"He's a big cat.
Come in and see him."

"All right," said Peter.
"I'll take a look at your cat.
But then I have to go right home."

Peter liked Jimmy's cat.
He forgot about going home.
The three boys had lots of fun.
And they played all afternoon.

Then it was time to go home.

Jimmy said, "Can we play
at your house next time, Peter?
I want to see your frog."

"All right," said Peter.
"But don't come with your cat.
Frogs don't like cats."

After that the three boys were
good friends.
Sometimes they played at Peter's house.
Sometimes they went to Edward's house.
And sometimes they went to Jimmy's house.

People said, "Edward and Peter
and Jimmy are like brothers."

And they were!

I live in an apartment house with my
mother and daddy my mother said she
wants me to go to the store for
her I will get some cookies daddy likes
them too mother wants some apples she will
make something good with the apples

I live in an apartment house with my
mother and daddy. My mother said she
wants me to go to the store for
her. I will get some cookies. Daddy likes
them, too. Mother wants some apples. She will
make something good with the apples.

Punctuation Cues. Have the first paragraph read. Discuss missing capital
letters and periods. Then have the children turn their books around and
read the same paragraph with punctuation. Explain that knowing where a
sentence begins and ends helps us to read with greater understanding.

47

That's What Friends Are For

Florence Parry Heide and Sylvia Worth Van Clief

Teddy has a bad leg.
And this is the day he was going
to see his cousin!

"What can I do?" Teddy asks.
"I can't go to my cousin's now.
I can't walk on my bad leg.
I'll ask my friends.
They will tell me what to do.
That's what friends are for," says Teddy.

Then Teddy's friend the bird comes by.

"What are you doing here?"
asks the bird.

"I have a bad leg, and I can't walk.
And I can't go to see my cousin,"
says Teddy.

"If I had a bad leg," says the bird,
"I would fly to see my cousin."

"Thank you for telling me
what to do," says Teddy.

"That's what friends are for,"
says the bird.

Then Teddy's friend the daddy longlegs comes by.

"What are you doing here?" asks the daddy longlegs.

"I have a bad leg, and I can't walk.
And I can't fly.
And I can't go to see my cousin,"
says Teddy.

"If I had a bad leg,"
says the daddy longlegs,
"I would walk.
I have lots of legs."

"Thank you for telling me
what to do," says Teddy.

"That's what friends are for,"
says the daddy longlegs.

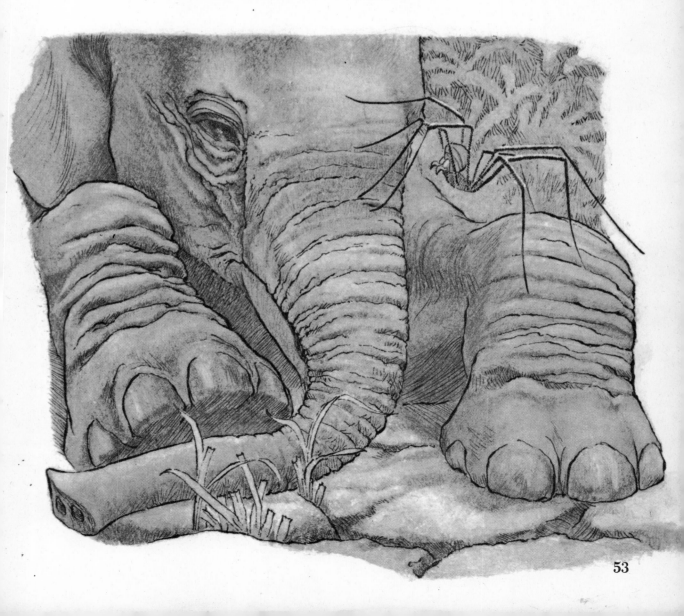

Then Teddy's friend the monkey
comes by.

"What are you doing here?"
asks the monkey.

"I have a bad leg, and I can't walk.
And I can't fly.
And I don't have lots of legs.
And I can't go to see my cousin,"
says Teddy.

"If I had a bad leg," says the monkey,
"I would go from tree to tree like this."

"Thank you for telling me what to do,"
says Teddy.

"That's what friends are for,"
says the monkey.

Then Teddy's friend the crab comes by.

"What are you doing here?"
asks the crab.

"I have a bad leg, and I can't walk.
And I can't fly.
And I don't have lots of legs.
And I can't go from tree to tree
by my tail.
And I can't go to see my cousin,"
says Teddy.

"If I had a bad leg," says the crab,
"I would get a new one."

"Thank you for telling me
what to do," says Teddy.

"That's what friends are for,"
says the crab.

Then Teddy's friend the raccoon
comes by.

"What is all the noise?" he asks.

"Teddy has a bad leg," says the bird.
"He can't fly."

"He can't go to see his cousin,"
says the crab.

"We are telling him what to do,"
says the monkey.

"That's what friends are for,"
says the daddy longlegs.

"No," says the raccoon.
"Friends are to help!"

"Help?" asks the bird.

"Yes," says the raccoon.
"You can help Teddy.
Go and get his cousin.
Tell him to come here to see Teddy."

All the friends go to find
Teddy's cousin.
When they come back,
Teddy's cousin is with them.

"Thank you for helping me,"
says Teddy.

61

To give advice is very nice,
but friends can do much more.
Friends should always help a friend.
That's what friends are for!

—Florence Parry Heide,
  Sylvia Worth Van Clief

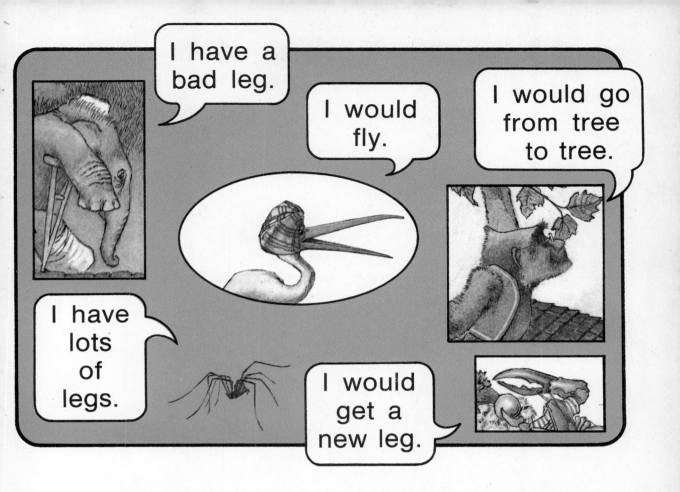

What Did You Say?

"I have a bad leg," said Teddy.
"I would fly," said the bird.
"I would go from tree to tree," said the monkey.
"I have lots of legs," said the daddy longlegs.
"I would get a new leg," said the crab.

The Little Red Flower

Paul Tripp

Trees and flowers didn't grow
in the small town.
There were cars and trucks
and houses and stores in the town.
There were lots of people and animals.
But no flowers and no trees
could grow there.

Then one day Mr. Greenthumb came
to live in the small town.
He came with a little red flower.
Mr. Greenthumb put the flower
in his window.
When the boys and girls came home
from school, they stopped to look at it.

"What is it?"

"It looks like a flower."

"It looks like a picture
I saw in a book."

The next morning people came
to see the little red flower.

"My boy was right," said a mother.
"It **is** a flower."

Then Mr. Greenthumb opened the window.
He put some water on his little flower.

"Did you see that?" asked a man.
"His thumb is green."

"That's what you have to have
to grow flowers," said a lady.

Mr. Greenthumb looked up
and saw all the people.

"Good morning," said a man.
"We came to see your flower.
We can't get flowers to grow
in this town."

"That's too bad," said Mr. Greenthumb.
"Would you all like to smell my flower?"

"Yes," said the people.

One by one they went up to the window.
They all loved the smell of the flower.

The people came to Mr. Greenthumb's house
every morning.
Mr. Greenthumb would open the window
and water the flower.
Then one by one the people would walk up
to the window and smell the flower.
And one by one they would walk back home
and say, "M-m-m, that flower smells good."

Every boy and girl made pictures
of the little red flower in school.
Every man went to work
and thought about the little red flower.
Every lady went home
and thought about the flower, too.
One man made lots of big signs.
The signs said, "To the Flower."
He put a sign on every street in town.

Who Can Save the Flower?

One morning Mr. Greenthumb
didn't come to the window.

"Where is he?" asked a boy.

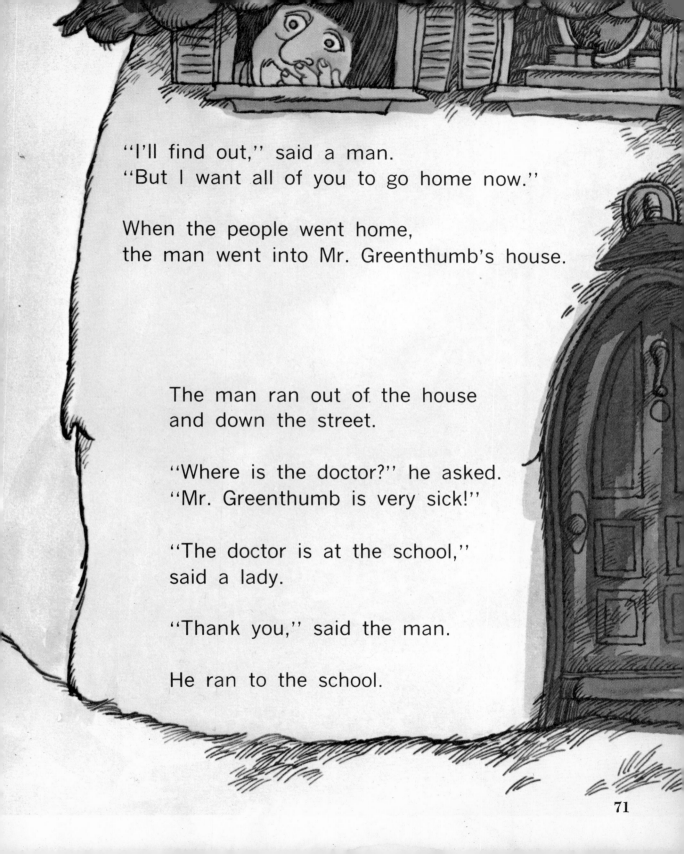

"I'll find out," said a man.
"But I want all of you to go home now."

When the people went home,
the man went into Mr. Greenthumb's house.

The man ran out of the house
and down the street.

"Where is the doctor?" he asked.
"Mr. Greenthumb is very sick!"

"The doctor is at the school,"
said a lady.

"Thank you," said the man.

He ran to the school.

All the people in the town ran
to Mr. Greenthumb's house.
The doctor went into the house.
The people waited all morning,
but the doctor didn't come out.
The people waited all afternoon,
but the doctor didn't come out.

Night came, and the doctor opened
the door.

"Mr. Greenthumb is very sick,"
he said to the people.
"He will be all right,
but someone will have to water his flower."

The people looked at the little red flower.
It looked very sick, too.

"You are a doctor," said a man.
"Can't you help the little red flower?"

"No," said the doctor.
"I'm a people doctor,
not a flower doctor.
One of **you** will have to save
Mr. Greenthumb's flower."

The doctor went back
into the house.

"Who can save the little red flower?"
asked a lady.

"Someone with a green thumb,"
said a man.

"I can do it,"
said the doctor's little boy.
"I'll try to save the little flower."

"You can't save it," said a man.
"You don't have a green thumb."

"Let the boy try," said a lady.

"Yes, let him try," said all the people.

That night the doctor sat
by Mr. Greenthumb's bed.
And his little boy sat
by the little red flower.
He put water on the flower
and went to sleep.

New Flowers

Day after day the little boy sat
by the flower.
The people came by the house
to look at the flower.
They waited for Mr. Greenthumb
to come to the window.
When he didn't come, they went home.

One day the people went
to Mr. Greenthumb's house.
The door opened, and out came
the doctor and Mr. Greenthumb.
The people were very happy
to see Mr. Greenthumb again.
And Mr. Greenthumb was happy
to be out of bed and with his friends.

Then the doctor's little boy came out
with the little red flower.

"Look!" said the boy.
"I did save the little flower."

"And he did it without a green thumb,"
said a man.

"Mr. Greenthumb," said the boy,
"look at your thumb.
It isn't green.
We thought you had a green thumb."

Mr. Greenthumb looked down at his thumb.
"The paint is gone," he said.

"What paint?" asked a man.

"I had green paint on my thumb,"
said Mr. Greenthumb.

All the people laughed.

"You don't have to have a green thumb
to grow flowers," said Mr. Greenthumb.
"Now, who wants to try to grow
a little flower?
I have seeds for all of you."

Every boy and girl wanted to try
to grow flowers from the seeds.

81

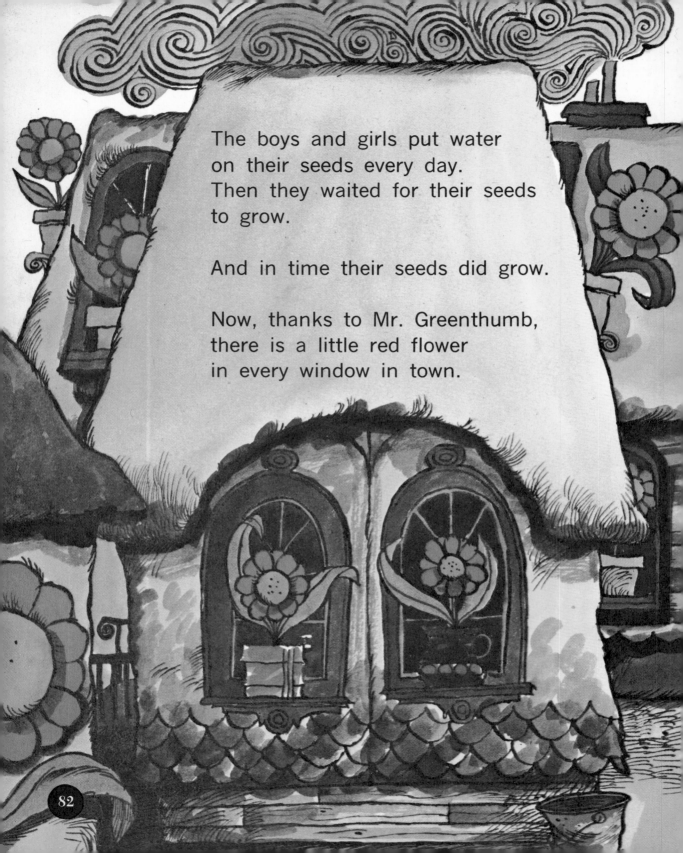

The boys and girls put water
on their seeds every day.
Then they waited for their seeds
to grow.

And in time their seeds did grow.

Now, thanks to Mr. Greenthumb,
there is a little red flower
in every window in town.

At Mrs. Appleby's

When frost is shining on the trees,
 It's spring at Mrs. Appleby's.
You smell it in the air before
 You step inside the kitchen door.

 Rows of scarlet flowers bloom
  From every window in the room.
 And funny little speckled fish
  Are swimming in a china dish.

A tiny bird with yellow wings
 Just sits and sings and sings and SINGS!
Outside when frost is on the trees,
 It's spring at Mrs. Appleby's.

—Elizabeth Upham McWebb

Whose Is It?

Jimmy's

Mrs. Appleby's

Rosa's

Mr. Greenthumb's

Edward's

Teddy's

Punctuation Cues. Match objects with their owners. Discuss the use of the apostrophe to show ownership.

All Kinds of Families

Freddy in the Middle

Judy Blume

Freddy had a big brother, Mike,
and a little sister, Ellen.
Freddy was the one in the middle.
He didn't like it.
He thought about it a lot.
But what could he do?

Every time Mike got too big
for his old clothes, he got new ones.
Then Freddy got Mike's old clothes.
No new clothes for Freddy!

Ellen had her own room.
But not Freddy!
He had to sleep in a room with Mike.

Freddy tried to play with Mike
and his friends.

But Mike said, "Go play
with your own friends.
This is a game for big boys."

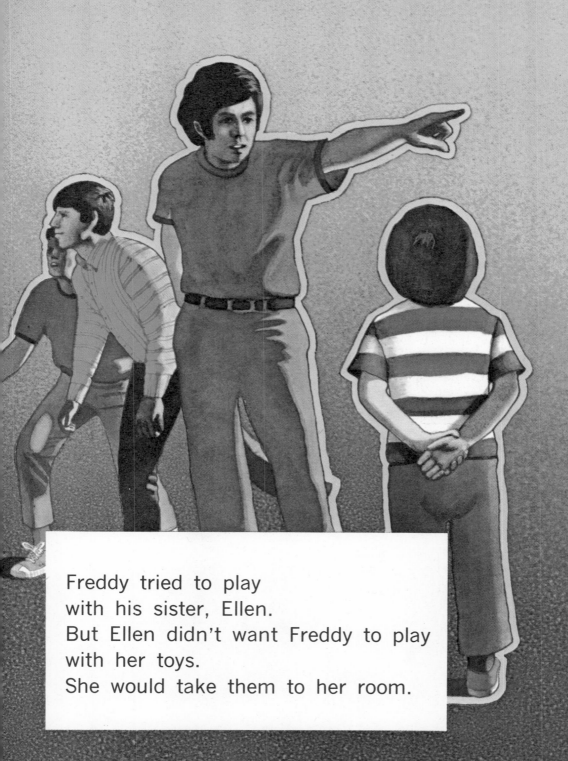

Freddy tried to play
with his sister, Ellen.
But Ellen didn't want Freddy to play
with her toys.
She would take them to her room.

Freddy's mother would come
into the room.

"Ellen won't let me play
with her toys," said Freddy.

"Ellen is too little to play with you.
You play with your own toys,"
said Mother.

Freddy couldn't play with Mike,
and he couldn't play with Ellen.
He was in the middle.

"And that," thought Freddy,
"is a bad place to be."

Freddy Gets a Part

One morning Freddy saw a sign
in school.
The sign said,

"That's for me," said Freddy.
"I'll ask Mrs. Cook
if I can be in the play."

Freddy ran to his room.

"Mrs. Cook," said Freddy.
"I want to be in the school play."

"The school play is for the big boys and girls," said Mrs. Cook.

"I see," said Freddy.

Freddy looked down at the floor and walked to the back of the room.

The next morning Mrs. Cook had
good news for Freddy.
She waited for him to come
into the room.

When he came in, she said,
"Mrs. Jay wants to see you
this afternoon, Freddy.
She may have a part for you
in the school play."

"Thank you, Mrs. Cook," said Freddy.

That afternoon Freddy went
to a big room to see Mrs. Jay.

"I'm Freddy," he said.
"And I want to be in your play."

"Go up on the stage, Freddy,
and say that again," said Mrs. Jay.

Freddy went up on the big stage.
He looked out at Mrs. Jay.

"I'm Freddy," he said.
"And I want to be in your play."

"Good," said Mrs. Jay.

"Now, Freddy," said Mrs. Jay.
"Can you jump?"

"Can I **jump**?" said Freddy.

Freddy did big jumps.

Then he did little jumps.

Then he did big jumps again.

Freddy could jump all right.

"Good, Freddy," said Mrs. Jay.
"You will make a good kangaroo."

"Kangaroo  " asked Freddy.

"A green kangaroo," said Mrs. Jay.
"Your part in the play will be
the Green Kangaroo."

The One in the Middle Is the Green Kangaroo

That night Freddy said,
"I got a part in the school play.
I'm going to be the Green Kangaroo."

"The Green Kangaroo?" laughed Mike.
He laughed so much, he couldn't stop.

When Ellen saw Mike laughing,
she laughed, too.
But Freddy was so happy, he didn't care.

"Good for you, Freddy," said Daddy.

And Mother said, "I'm so happy
for you, Freddy."

Freddy worked on his kangaroo jumps
every day.
He did kangaroo jumps on the stage
at school.
And he did them on his bed at home.

One night Mike came into the room.
He saw Freddy jumping on the bed.

"What are you doing?" asked Mike.

"I'm the Green Kangaroo!" said Freddy.

Then the day of the play came.
Freddy went to Mrs. Jay's room
in the afternoon.
The big girls helped Freddy get
into his kangaroo clothes.
Freddy jumped all over the room.

"I'm the Green Kangaroo," he said.

The boys and girls laughed.
And so did Mrs. Jay.

It was time for the play.
Freddy jumped out on the stage.
His mother and daddy had come
to see the play.
So had Mike and Ellen and Mrs. Cook.
They were in the middle of all the people.
But not Freddy!
He was alone on the stage.

"Hello,"

said Freddy.

"I'm the Green Kangaroo."

The play went on.
Freddy did his little jumps.
He jumped all over the stage.

Someone would ask,
"And who are you?"

And Freddy would say,

"I'm the Green Kangaroo."

Every time Freddy said that,
the people would laugh.
Freddy liked it when they laughed.

Then the play was over.
The big boys and girls came out
on the stage.

Mrs. Jay came out and said,
"I want to thank little Freddy.
He played the part of the Green Kangaroo."

Freddy came out on the stage.
He was not the one in the middle now.
He was all alone.
It was Freddy's big day.

After that Freddy didn't care
if he got Mike's old clothes.
He didn't care if Ellen had
her own room.
And he didn't care about being
the one in the middle.
Being Freddy was not so bad after all.

Just About

I'm just about ready
   To turn to a gnome.
I'm tired of staying
   So close to home.

I'm just about ready
   To turn to an elf.
I'm quite tired of being
   Only myself.

I'm just about ready
   To turn to a sprite,
But I'll be myself, home again,
   Long before night.

—Leland B. Jacobs

Short Cut

Mr. Bob's Button Co.

Park Ave.

Green St.

Dr. Brown

Mrs. Baker's Tea Room
open Mon. - Sat.

Abbreviations. Have children find abbreviations in the street scene. Write the unabbreviated words and the abbreviations on the board for comparison. Point out use of capital letters and periods in these abbreviations.

107

Eleanor Clymer

The New Spring Hats

It was spring.
Birds were singing.
Flowers were everywhere.
And all the ladies had new spring hats.

"I would like a new spring hat, too,"
Belinda said to her mother.

"You would?" asked Mother.
"I'll get one for you."

"When?" asked Belinda.

"When I have some time," said Mother.
"I can't get one for you now.
You will have to wait."

Belinda waited.
All the time she was playing
and going to school, she waited.

One day Belinda said,
"I'll have to find my own hat."

So Belinda looked all over the house.
Then she saw a good hat.
She put it on her head
and went to show her mother.

"Belinda!" said Mother.
"What is that on your head?"

"It's my new spring hat,"
said Belinda.
"Do you like it?"

"Very much," said her mother.
"But it looks a little like a bowl."

Belinda looked in the mirror.
Her spring hat did look like a bowl.
So she put it back
and went to find another one.

"Here is a good hat," she said.

She put it on and went to show her aunt.

"Hello, Belinda," said her aunt.
"What is that on your head?"

"It's my new spring hat,"
said Belinda.
"Is it all right?"

"Yes it is," said Belinda's aunt.
"I like it very much.
But isn't it too big?"

Belinda tried to look in the mirror.
But she couldn't see.
Her aunt was right.

"This hat is much too big for me,"
said Belinda.

So she put it on the floor
and went to find another hat.

Belinda's Hat

Belinda found another hat.
She liked this one very much.
She put it on and went to show Grandma.

"Belinda," said Grandma.
"What is that on your head?"

"It's my new spring hat,"
said Belinda.
"I found it.
Do you like it?"

"I do," said Grandma.
"But it looks a little like the box
the cat sleeps in."

Belinda looked in the mirror.

"You are right, Grandma," she said.
"I can't wear this."

Belinda put the box back on the floor,
and the cat got into it.

Belinda walked out of the house.

"I have to find a hat to wear
for spring," she said.
"Maybe I'll find one out here."

By the time her daddy came home,
Belinda had found a new hat.

"Hello, Belinda," said Daddy.
"What is that on your head?"

"It's my new spring hat,"
said Belinda.
"Do you like it?"

"Yes," said her daddy.
"There won't be another girl in town
with a hat like that."

Belinda laughed.

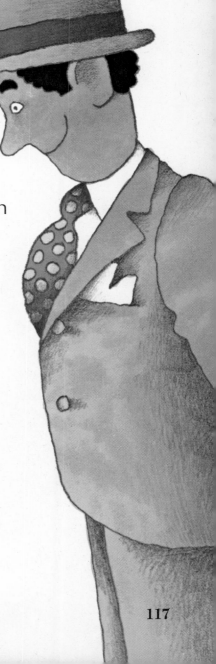

"What have you got there, Daddy?"
Belinda asked.

"This is a plant for Mother.
Would you like to help me put it
in a flower pot?" asked Daddy.

"Yes," said Belinda.
"But where is the flower pot?"

"It's in the box," said Daddy.
"Open it."

Belinda opened the box.

"What is this?" she asked.

"It's the flower pot," said Daddy.

"Daddy," said Belinda.
"You can't put the plant in that!"

"No," said Daddy.
"Maybe you are right.
But what will we do with the plant?
I can't get another flower pot now."

"Take my hat," said Belinda.

"All right," said Daddy.
"But you will have to wear
the flower pot."

"I would love to," said Belinda.

And she went to show her mother,
her aunt, and her grandma
her new spring hat.

Nobody's Nicer

Nobody's nicer
than Mrs. King.

She came to visit
one day in spring,
and let me flash
with her diamond ring.

And even better,
she let me wear
her amber comb
in my yellow hair.

But best of all . . .
you should have seen!
I tried on her earrings,
and looked sixteen.

—Aileen Fisher

Two Into One

let us   let's

that is   that's

is not   isn't

we are   we're

Contractions. Discuss illustrations. Note two words at the beginning of each set and one word at the end. Call attention to the missing letters and the use of the apostrophe.

Liesel Moak Skorpen

All the Lassies

"I would like a dog," said Peter.

"I know you would," said his mother,
"but we don't have room for a dog."

"Just a little dog," said Peter.

"No," said his mother,
"but you can have a fish."

Peter named his fish 𝕷assie.
He tried to make the fish come to him
when he called.

"Here, Lassie," called Peter.
"Here, Lassie, old girl."

But the fish didn't come.

"I would like a dog," said Peter.

"I know you would," said his mother,
"but we don't have room for a dog."

"Just a little one?" asked Peter.

"No," said his mother,
"but you can have a turtle."

125

Peter named his turtle **Lassie.**
He wanted the turtle to wag its tail.
All morning Peter tried to make
the turtle wag its tail.

"Come on, Lassie," said Peter.
"Wag your tail."

But the turtle didn't wag its tail.

"I would like a dog," said Peter.

"Don't you like your turtle?"
asked his mother.

"I like it very much," said Peter,
"but I would like to have a dog."

"I'll ask your daddy," said his mother.
"Maybe you can have a bird."

127

Peter named his bird **Lassie.**
He tried to make the bird say,
''Woof, woof.''
But all the bird could say was,

"Tweet,

tweet."

All the Lassies and Walter

"I would like a dog," said Peter.

"I know you would," said his mother,
"but we don't have room for a dog."

"All I want is a little dog," said Peter.

"I know someone who has two kittens,"
said his mother.
"Maybe I can get one for you."

Peter named his kitten Lassie.

"I'll throw the ball, Lassie,
and you bring it back to me," said Peter.

The kitten ran to get the ball.
But she didn't bring it back to Peter.
Peter picked up the kitten.

"You are a good kitten, but not a good dog,"
said Peter.

That night Peter's mother came into his room to say good night.

"Mother," said Peter.
"I would like to have a dog."

"All right," said his mother.
"You may have a very little dog."

131

The next day Peter and his mother went
to the pet store.
They came home with a very big dog.
The dog came when Peter called him.
He could wag his tail.
He could say,

"WOOF,
WOOF."

When Peter would throw the ball,
the dog would bring it back.

Peter named the dog **WALTER.**
Walter made very good friends
with all the Lassies.

Bert's Berries

George McCue

Big Bert liked to eat.
All bears do.
But Bert was not like
all the other bears.
Bert liked to eat berries.
Not fish!
Not any of the other things bears eat!
Just berries!

But in winter it was cold.
It was too cold for berries.
So Bert sat in his cave
and thought about berries.

All the other bears went to sleep.
They would sleep all winter.
But not Bert!
He sat in the cold cave
and thought about berries.

One day when winter was over,
Bert ran from his cave.

"It's time for berries again!" he said.

But when Bert found the berries,
they were too green to eat.
So he waited.
Every day he went to look at the berries.

One day he said,
"The berries look good.
They are not so green now.
In about one day I can eat them."

There was no sleep for Bert that night.
He thought about all the berries
he would eat in the morning.

When morning came, Bert ran to the berries.
But what did he find?
Some of his berries were gone!

"Who would do that?" Bert thought.
"Who would eat my berries?"

There were lots of berries for Bert.
But he didn't care.
He didn't want lots of berries.
He wanted **all** the berries!

"I have to find out who is eating
my berries," said Bert.
"I know what I'll do.
I'll climb a tree near the berries.
No one will see me if I climb a tree.
But I can see who is eating my berries."

Bert found a good tree to climb.
All that day he waited in the tree
near the berries.
And all that night he waited.
He was very quiet.
But no one came near the berries.

A Happy Bear

The next morning Bert saw something
near the berries.
It was a fox.
And the fox began to eat Bert's berries.

"Stop it! Stop it!" said Bert.

The fox looked up in the tree
and saw Big Bert.

"Why do you want me to stop?"
he asked.
"I don't eat very much.
Why can't I have some of the berries?"

"Because I want them all," said Big Bert.
"Now get out of there.
I don't have to let you eat my berries."

"If I go, the rabbits will come,"
said the fox.
"And then you will have no berries at all."

Bert began to laugh.
"There are no rabbits here," he said.

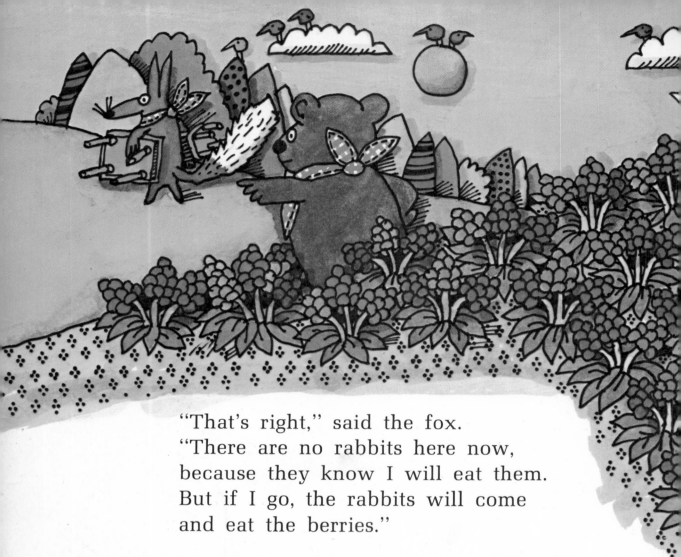

"That's right," said the fox.
"There are no rabbits here now,
because they know I will eat them.
But if I go, the rabbits will come
and eat the berries."

Bert laughed at the fox again.

"The rabbits will not come here
when they see me," said Big Bert.
"Now get out and don't let me see you
near my berries again."

And so the fox had to go.

Bert was very happy
because all the berries were his.
And then he saw a rabbit.
Then two rabbits!
Then three!
Then everywhere he looked,
he saw a rabbit.
And they were all eating his berries!

"Stop it! Stop it!" said Bert.

The rabbits went right on eating.
Bert ran after them.
But he couldn't get near the rabbits.
He was too big.
He tried and tried.
But he didn't get one rabbit.
He had to stop and sit down.

The rabbits began to laugh at Bert.
And that did not make Bert a happy bear.

"What can I do?" thought Bert.
"I know," he said.
"I will go and find the fox."
And that's what he did.

"Fox," said Bert, "come back with me.
You can have some of my berries."

"Why do you want me now?"
asked the fox.

"Because you were right," said Bert.
"The rabbits did come.
They will eat all the berries
if you don't stop them.
Will you come back?" asked Bert.

"Thank you," said the fox.
"I will."

And he went back to the berries.

When the rabbits saw the fox, they ran.
And they didn't come back again.

The fox had all the berries he wanted.
And Bert had all the berries he wanted.
And he could laugh at the rabbits.
That made Bert a very happy bear.

The Family in Art

The family is found in many great works of art.
Each artist shows the family in his own way.

The Boating Party
MARY CASSATT

Mary Cassatt painted this picture of a family
having fun together. She shows you how they feel
by the way they are looking at each other.

Mother and Child

CHARLES WHITE

Charles White drew this picture with a pencil.
He made the faces and hands of the mother and
her baby the most important part of the picture.
Can you see how he did it?

146

A Japanese artist painted this picture. It shows
a mother teaching her baby to walk. Many great
paintings show families doing everyday things.

Potted Tree from the Kame-ya,
one of "The Women in Summer Dresses"
KITAGAWA UTAMARO

Renoir painted this portrait of a mother and her two little girls. In a portrait the artist paints people the way they really look, just as if he were taking their picture with a camera. Even the dog got into this family portrait.

Madame Charpentier and Her Children

PIERRE AUGUSTE RENOIR

Rocking Chair No. 2

HENRY MOORE

Henry Moore made this metal sculpture of a mother
rocking her baby. Notice how smooth and rounded
he made them. That's the way this artist
likes to work.

LINDA FERRAN, BROOKLYN, NEW YORK

An artist in the first grade did this crayon drawing
of her family. Some grown-up artists use
crayons, too.

Isi and His Sons

An Egyptian artist carved a father and his sons
in a huge block of stone. He made the father much
bigger than his sons to show how important he was.

KAZIMIERZ MICHALOWSKI, *L'ART DE L'ANCIENNE EGYPTE*, EDITIONS D'ART
LUCIEN MAZENOD, PARIS

151

The Walk to Paradise Garden

W. EUGENE SMITH

A photographer took this picture of his children
when they were walking in the woods one day.
You can't see their faces, but can you tell how they
feel about each other?

A Quiet Walk

When I take Peg to walk,
We hardly ever talk.
There's just too much to see.
I like to laugh and play,
But—somehow--not today.
And Peg feels just like me.
We're quiet when we walk
For we don't need to talk.
There's just too much to see.

—Pete Shiflet

bear
bears

fox
foxes

berry
berries

One or More?

lady   ball   box
ladies   balls   boxes

wish   bunny   rabbit
wishes   bunnies   rabbits

Plural Forms. Have numbered pairs of words read. Point out how the plural for each pair was formed. Have other pairs of words read. Let children decide if the plural was formed as in 1, 2, or 3.

154

Three Guesses

hat
hit
hot

bad   bed   bud

leg   log   lag

fin   fan   fun

pet
put
pot

net
not
nut

Medial Vowel Substitution. Have the three words in each box read. Ask which word goes with the picture.

All Kinds of Places to Go

Herman and the Bears

Bernice Myers

Little Herman
went to see
his aunt.

It was a
very
cold
day.

Herman
was wearing
his long fur coat
and
big fur hat.

He looked
just like
a bear.

And that is what
a small bear
thought
he looked like.

"Cousin Julius,"
said the bear,
and he ran
with Herman
to his cave.

"Look who
I found,"
he called.

All the bears
ran over
to say
hello.

"Cousin Julius,
Cousin Julius,"
they said.

"I'm Herman,"
said Herman.
"I'm not a bear."

But it was time
to eat.
So no one heard him.

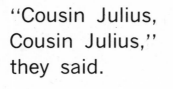

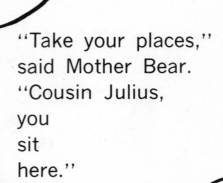

"Take your places,"
said Mother Bear.
"Cousin Julius,
you
sit
here."

All the bears
began
to eat
their soup
right out of the
bowl.

But not Herman.

He had a spoon.
And he
began
to eat his soup
with the spoon.

The bears laughed.
"That's a
good trick
for a bear."

"I'm not a bear!
I'm a boy . . ."

But no one heard
him.
They made
too much
noise
eating their soup.

"I'll show them
I'm a boy!"
said Herman.

He did
all the tricks
a boy
can do.

But the bears
just laughed.

"It's like
being at
a carnival,"
said
Mother Bear.

"Teach us.
Teach us, too,
Cousin Julius,"
said the bears.

And they
jumped
all over him.

"What a
cousin
we have,"
said Mother
Bear.

Not This Bear!

After Herman
did his tricks,
Father Bear
went to look
out of
the cave.

"It's winter,"
he said.
"Time to go
to sleep.

"Don't forget,
my little bears,
we sleep
all winter."

"All winter?"
said Herman.

"I sleep
one night
at a time.
I like to play
all day.
I'm not sleeping
all winter."

"But all bears do,"
said a little bear.

"Not **this** bear," said Herman.
"I like winter."

"He **likes** winter,"
said a bear.

"Yes," said Herman.
"It's fun.
I like it
when it's cold.
I like
winter games.
And I do have
to go to school,
you know."

The bears
looked at him.

Then Father Bear said,
"Now that I look
at you,
you don't look
like a bear.
You don't look
like us at all!"

A little Bear
went over
to Herman.

Off came
Herman's
fur coat
and hat.

"You are not
a bear!"

"That's what
I tried
to tell you,"
said Herman.
"Now may I
have
my coat back?
I'm cold!"

167

Herman put on
his fur coat
and his fur hat
and said
good-by
to all the bears.

"Come
and see us
in the spring," 'they said.

"I will,"
called Herman.

And off he went
to his
aunt's house.

When Herman
walked by a
big tree,
a happy bear
jumped out.

"Cousin Bernard,
Cousin Bernard,"
he called.

Herman ran
and ran
and
ran
without stopping.

169

When he
did stop,
he had
reached
his aunt's house.
And
there she was,
waiting
for
him
at the
door.

The Browns Say Good-by

Moving day had come.
The Browns were going
to another town.
They were all waiting
for the moving truck.
Mrs. Brown was putting
some clothes into a big box.
Mr. Brown was putting
some boxes into the car.

Bobby had gone down the street
to say good-by to his friends.
He gave his goldfish
to his friend Jay.
He gave his turtle
to his friend Ben.
And he gave his frog
to his friend Mike.

When Bobby got home, he saw
some people who lived on his street.
They had come to say good-by
to the Browns.
Old Mrs. Cook had come with cookies
for Bobby and his sister, Jenny.
Mr. Green had come with some seeds
for Bobby to plant at his new house.

Just then the moving truck
came down the street.
After all the boxes were put
into the big truck, it was time to go.
Bobby didn't want to go.
He ran to the big tree
in back of the house and climbed up.
Bobby's father ran after him.

"Come down from there, Bobby,"
said his father.
"It's time to go."

"I'm not going," said Bobby.
"I won't have any friends.
And there won't be any trees to climb.
And I don't want to go to a new school."

"I saw lots of boys and girls
for you to play with," said his father.
"There's a school just down the street
from the new house.
And there's a big tree right
in back of the house."

Bobby climbed down from the tree
and walked to the car with his father.

"I'll take a look
at the new house," said Bobby.
"But I'm not going to live there.
I don't want to live in any house
but this one."

Bobby was not happy about moving,
but he got into the car.
He looked out the window
at the house and the big tree.
The moving truck had gone.
And the Browns were off
to their new home.

The New House

That afternoon the Browns got
to their new house.
Bobby and Jenny got out of the car
and ran into the house.
They opened all the doors
and looked in all the rooms.
All the rooms smelled of new paint.

Jenny found a good place
in her room for her toys.
Mrs. Brown came in to help her
take them out of the boxes.
Then she went into Bobby's room.

"Do you like your room, Bobby?"
asked Mrs. Brown.

"It's a good room," said Bobby.
"But it's not like my old room.
I'll sleep here tonight.
Then I'm moving back
to our old house."

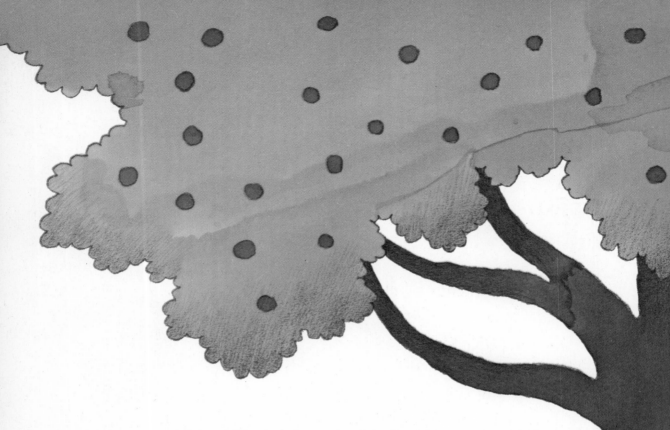

Bobby looked out the bedroom window
and saw a big tree.

"That looks like a good tree,"
he said to his mother.
"But it's not like the tree
back at our old house.
It's just not the same.
There's no treehouse in this one.
I'll climb the tree in the morning,
just to see what it's like.
But then I'm going back to my old tree."

The next morning Bobby was playing
in the big tree.
Two boys came by and stopped
when they saw him.

"What are you doing up in that tree?"
asked one of the boys.
"That's our tree."

"No it isn't," said Bobby.
"It's my tree now.
It came with the house.
That's my house, and this is my tree."

"Come on, Dan," said one boy.
"We can find another tree."

The two boys began to walk
up the street.

"Wait!" said Bobby.
"There's room for you in the tree.
Climb up."

So the two boys climbed up the tree.
And the three boys played games
in the tree all morning.

Jenny found her own friends.
One friend had lots of hats.
Jenny loved hats, and she couldn't wait
to try them on.
Another friend had some kittens.
After Jenny tried on the hats,
she went to play with the kittens.
Jenny was happy in the new house.

That night Bobby's father came
into his room.

"Do you want to go back
to our old house?" he asked.
"I'll take you back any time you say."

"Not tonight," said Bobby.
"I thought it over.
I have lots of work to do here.
I have to plant my seeds.
And I have to make a treehouse.
And I have to get some new pets.
If my pets like my new room,
maybe I'll live here after all."

It didn't take long for Bobby
and his friends to make a treehouse.
It looked the same as Bobby's old one.

And it didn't take long for Bobby's new room
to look the same as the old one.
And by then Bobby didn't want
to go back to the old house.
The new house was just right for him.

New Neighbors

When Smiths packed up
and moved away,
and Judy was gone,
I cried all day.

I knew I'd never
like anyone
as much as Judy
or have such fun.

Then Browns moved in
with a silky cat
and a dog with puppies.
Imagine that!

And a girl named Becky . . .
and I forgot
all about missing
Judy a lot.

—Aileen Fisher

186

Help from Space

Can you read this?

Movingdayhadcome.

Let's add spaces.

Moving day had come.

Now can you read it?

Moving day had come.

Space between words makes sentences easier to read.

Try to read these sentences.

TheBrownsweregoingtoanothertown.
Theywereallwaitingforthemovingtruck.

Now read the sentences again.

The Browns were going to another town.
They were all waiting for the moving truck.

Space as a Cue. Call attention to space as a way of making reading easy.
Compare the two versions of the sample sentences.

187

Our Trip

Annie Moorecroft

I'm Sandy Edwards.
I have a mother and a father
and a big brother, Jimmy.
This is about the time
we all went on a trip to Washington.

It takes a day to get there
by car from where we live.

Jimmy and I were sitting
in the back of the car.
My mother was sitting with my father.
I didn't have much fun that day.
I had to sit next to Jimmy all day.

Jimmy knows a lot,
and he likes to show off.

"There are two Washingtons,"
Jimmy said to me.
"One is a city, and one is a state.
Do you know the one we are going to?"

I didn't know anything about Washington.
But I didn't want Jimmy to know that.
So I didn't say anything to him.
I just looked out the window.

"You don't know anything, do you?"
said Jimmy.
"We are going to the city of Washington.
That's Washington, D.C.
We can't go to the state of Washington.
It's so far from here
it would take us two days to get there."

"The state of Washington is too far
to get there in two days,"
said my father.

"See?" I said to Jimmy.
"You don't know so much."

"Do you know that Washington was named
for someone?" asked Jimmy.

"Everyone knows that," I said.
"It was named for George Washington.
And I know that the White House is
in Washington, too."

"Yes, but George Washington didn't live
in it," Jimmy said.

"Who said he did live in it?" I asked.
"And get out of my place.
Mother, he's got his legs
in my part of the car."

Mother said, "Now, Sandy."

"Jimmy," said my father.
"Can't you and Sandy be good
when we go on a trip?"

"Sandy," said my mother.
"Come up here with me
and get some sleep.
We won't get to our motel
for a long time."

So I did.
I was sleeping when the car
stopped at our motel.

Washington, D.C.

The motel part of the trip was fun.
Jimmy and my father put our clothes
in our motel room.
Little beds were put up just for us.
We all got back into the car
and went to see the city.

We all thought Washington was
a beautiful city.
We went back to the motel
and thought about all the places
we wanted to see the next day.

The next day we went to the White House.
It's a beautiful place.
Then we stopped to look
at the cherry trees.
They had flowers all over them.
I wanted to take some back
to our motel room.
But my mother said I couldn't.

My father told us that
the Washington Monument was not too far
from the White House.
So we walked from the White House
to the Monument.
The Washington Monument goes
up and up.
And you can see all over the city
from the Monument.
Jimmy thought that was the best part
of the trip.

But the very best part for me
was at night.
We went back to the cherry trees.
My father said, "Look."
And there in back of the trees
I saw the Washington Monument.
There were lots of lights near it.

"Isn't that beautiful!" said Mother.

She had my hand and Jimmy's.
I put my other hand in Daddy's.
And there we were, in the night,
looking at that light.
That was the very best part
of my trip to Washington.

199

Slow Down!

A comma says, "Slow down but don't stop."

One day after school, Bobby wanted to play.

He went to see his friend, Jim.

"Let's have something to eat," said Jim.

The boys had apples, cookies, and milk.

Punctuation Cues. Read the first sentence to the children. Discuss the illustration and then have the sentences read, listening for the pause for commas.

The Camel Who Went for a Walk

Jack Tworkov

It was that quiet time in the forest.
Night was just about over.
All the forest animals were sleeping.
No one was moving.
Everything was very, very quiet.

The tiger had been sleeping
by a tree near the road.
Just then he opened his eyes.
The tiger heard something.
And he saw what it was.
It was a camel.

A beautiful camel with brown eyes
was out for her morning walk.
As she walked, she stopped to smell
some of the forest flowers.
The tiger didn't take his eyes
off the camel as she came down the road.

"When she comes by this tree,"
he thought, "I will jump on her."

But the tiger was not the only one
who saw the camel walking down the road.
Up in the tree over the tiger
sat a little monkey.
The monkey saw what the tiger
was going to do.

So he reached for a coconut and said,
"When the tiger jumps on the camel,
I'll throw this coconut down on his head."

The beautiful camel didn't know
what was going on in the tree
in the forest.
So she walked on down the road.

But the tiger and the monkey were not
the only ones who saw the camel.
In the same tree a little squirrel
saw what was going on.
The squirrel climbed up
in back of the monkey.
The monkey's eyes were on the camel.
He didn't see the squirrel.

"When the monkey throws the coconut
at the tiger, I will bite the monkey's tail,"
said the squirrel.

The beautiful camel didn't know
what was going on in the tree
in the forest.
So she walked on down the road.

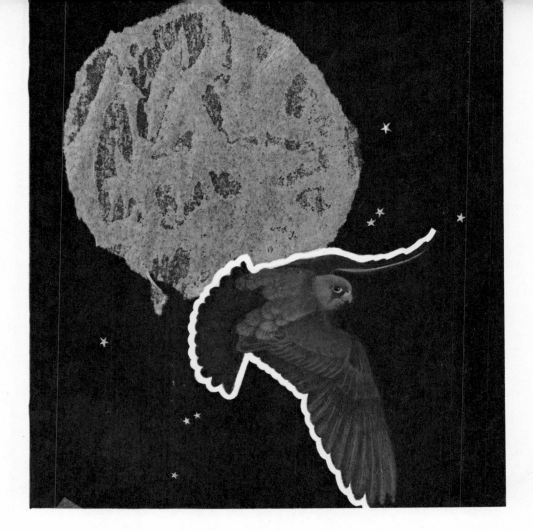

But the tiger, the monkey,
and the squirrel were not the only ones
who saw the camel.
A little bird saw what was going on.

"I know what I'll do," said the bird.
"When the squirrel bites the monkey's tail,
I will fly down on the squirrel's head."

The animals waited.
Everything was quiet.
Now the camel was very near the tree.
The tiger was about to jump.
The monkey was about to throw
the coconut.
The squirrel was about to bite.
And the bird was about to fly down.
But just then the camel stopped!

"It's time to go home now,"
said the camel.
"I have been gone too long."

And she walked back up the road.

The tiger just sat by the tree,
looking at the camel as she walked
back up the road.
He didn't jump on the camel.
And the monkey didn't throw
his coconut.
The squirrel didn't bite
the monkey's tail.
And the bird didn't jump
on the squirrel's head.
The animals didn't do anything.
They just sat where they were.

No one said anything.
No one made a noise.
Then the little bird began to laugh.
When the squirrel heard the bird,
he began to laugh, too.
The monkey began jumping up and down.
They made so much noise,
the other animals in the forest
couldn't sleep.

"What is going on?" asked a chipmunk.

"Not a thing," said the bird.

And he began to laugh all over again.

Camel

On the brown camel's back
    is a very big bump
And that is called
    a camel's hump.
He lives in the desert
    in a very hot land
And nibbles on palm leaves
    and sleeps on the sand.

—Nita Jonas

Margaret Wise Brown

Where Have You Been?

n. green

Little Old Cat
Little Old Cat
Where have you been?
To see this and that
Said the Little Old Cat
That's where I've been.

Little Old Squirrel
Little Old Squirrel
Where have you been?
I've been out on a whirl
Said the Little Old Squirrel
That's where I've been.

Little Old Fish
Little Old Fish
Where do you swim?
Wherever I wish
Said the Little Old Fish
That's where I swim.

Little Brown Bird
Little Brown Bird
Where do you fly?
I fly in the sky
Said the Little Brown Bird
That's where I fly.

Little Old Toad
Little Old Toad
Where have you been?
I've been way up the road
Said the Little Old Toad
That's where I've been.

Little Old Frog
Little Old Frog
Where have you been?
I've been sitting on a log
Said the Little Old Frog
That's where I've been.

Little Old Mole
Little Old Mole
Where have you been?
Down a long dark hole
Said the Little Old Mole
That's where I've been.

Little Old Bee
Little Old Bee
Where have you been?
In a pink apple tree
Said the Little Old Bee
That's where I've been.

Little Old Bunny
Little Old Bunny
Why do you run?
I run because it's fun
Said the Little Old Bunny
That's why I run.

Little Old Mouse
Little Old Mouse
Why run down the clock?
To see if the tick
Comes after the tock
I run down the clock.

Little Old Rook
Little Old Rook
Where do you look?
At the very last page
Of this very same book
Said the Little Old Rook.

New Words

The words listed beside the page numbers below are introduced in *A Time for Friends,* Level 8 in THE HOLT BASIC READING SYSTEM. Italicized words can be identified independently from previously taught skills.

14. Kim
    Rosa
15. apartment
    her
16. *Kim's*
    Rosa's
    take
    alone
20. elevator
    buttons
    reach
21. *button*
22. this
    floor
29. would
    nights
30. school
    worked
31. sometimes
    after
    brothers
32. *that's*
    bad
33. *wants*
35. lives
    has
    about
36. your
39. *he's*
    Jimmy's

41. walked
    fun
    without
44. *forgot*
49. leg
    cousin
50. *asks*
    cousin's
    walk
51. fly
    thank
    telling
52. longlegs
    legs
56. crab
59. help
60. *helping*
64. red
    grow
    town
    could
    Greenthumb
    live
65. *picture*
66. *thumb*
    green
67. smell
68. *Greenthumb's*
    every
    smells

69. thought
71. doctor
    very
72. waited
75. *doctor's*
    try
76. sat
79. happy
80. paint
81. seeds
82. their
    thanks
88. Freddy
    middle
    Mike
    Ellen
89. clothes
    ones
    Mike's
    own
    room
91. *toys*
92. *Freddy's*
93. part
    Mrs.
    Cook
96. stage
97. *jumps*
98. kangaroo
99. so

laughing
care
100. *jumping*
101. *Jay's*
helped
over
103. *laugh*
105. *being*
108. spring
hats
birds
singing
everywhere
109. *hat*
Belinda
wait
110. *head*
112. mirror
another
aunt
113. *Belinda's*
115. found
Grandma
116. wear
118. plant
pot
123. Lassies
know
just
fish
124. *Lassie*
called
125. turtle
126. wag
128. tweet
129. Walter
kittens

130. named
kitten
throw
ball
bring
134. Bert's
berries
Bert
other
any
things
winter
cold
cave
137. *eating*
climb
near
138. *something*
fox
began
139. why
because
rabbits
142. *sit*
158. Herman
wearing
long
fur
coat
159. Julius
160. heard
161. soup
spoon
163. teach
us
164. father
forget

167. off
Herman's
168. *aunt's*
169. Bernard
stopping
170. *reached*
waiting
171. *Browns*
moving
truck
putting
172. Bobby
gave
174. *climbed*
Bobby's
175. *there's*
178. *doors*
rooms
smelled
179. *tonight*
our
180. *bedroom*
same
treehouse
184. *pets*
as
188. trip
Edwards
Washington
takes
sitting
knows
Washingtons
state
189. *anything*
190. far
days